So what should you be zapping in the Annual?

Try It Now!

Wherever you see the interactive icon you'll be able to unlock a fun experience to enjoy on your device. There are nine scattered throughout the Annual and one on the front cover to discover. See if you can find them all.

ZAP NOW!

ID590279

Ready

Open Zappar on your device.

Aim

Scan the code on the page.

Zap

Then point your device at the page and watch it come to life!

A few helpful tips...

To get the best possible experience here are a few hints and tips:

- Connect to wifi if you can and the experiences will download even quicker than on 3G.
- Try and keep the pages as flat as you can for the best effect. Rest the Annual on a table or on the floor.
- Try and keep the full page in view from your phone after scanning the code. Don't get too close or far away if you can help it.

- Try and keep the pages clean and free from tears, pen and other marks as this may affect the experience.
- It's best to view the pages in good lighting conditions if you can.

If you're still having problems then do contact us at support@zappar.com and we'll do our best to help you.

CONTENTS

◒ UNLOCK BONUS INTERACTIVE PAGE!

ANGRY BIRDS™ & © 2009-2014
Rovio Entertainment Ltd.

© Lucasfilm Ltd. & ® or ™ where indicated.
All rights reserved.

Published 2014. Pedigree Books Limited, Beech Hill
House, Walnut Gardens, Exeter, Devon EX4 4DH.
www.pedigreebooks.com – books@pedigreegroup.co.uk
The Pedigree trademark, email and website addresses,
are the sole and exclusive properties of Pedigree Group
Limited, used under licence in this publication.

SOMEWHERE IN SPACE THERE IS A LOT OF ANGER...

Fighting the tyranny of the evil Pig Empire, brave Bird Rebels stole details of the Empire's latest weapon – the planet destroying Pig Star.

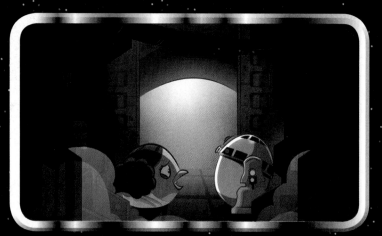

The plans were hidden on Princess Stella's starship. Before long, Stella's ship was intercepted by the evil Lard Vader and his Pigtroopers. Stella hid the plans in a brave droid called R2-EGG2 just before she was captured.

R2-EGG2 and his companion C-3PYOLK escaped Stella's ship. They soon found themselves in the hands of an aging Jedi Bird called Obi-Wan Kaboomi and his eager young apprentice, Red Skywalker. Red wanted to leave his farming job – he was a terrible farmer, after all. He longed for a life of adventure, especially after Obi-Wan explained that the evil Lard

Vader had killed his father!

Red joined Obi-Wan on his quest to rescue Princess Stella. Accompanied by the droids, the two brave birds booked passage on the *Mighty Falcon*, a smuggling spaceship and "the fastest hunk of bird droppings in the galaxy" — at least according to its captain, Chuck "Ham" Solo and his co-pilot, Terebacca! Chuck didn't mention that he was in a lot of trouble with a crime lord called Jabba the Hog — he just hoped that Jabba never caught up with him!

The heroic birds sneaked aboard the Pig Star and rescued Princess Stella from the prison cells. But while they were there, Obi-Wan sensed a presence he had not felt in many years his old pupil, Lard Vader.

Kaboomi and Vader met in a thrilling clash of lightsaber blades. When the battle was over Lard Vader stood victorious — old Obi-Wan was dead!

Chuck steered the group back to the *Mighty Falcon* and together they made a hasty escape from the Pig Star, chased by Pigfighter spaceships. But Red was really angry now and he joined the other pilots of the Bird Rebel Alliance in a determined assault on the Pig Star. Red struck the killer blow, destroying the evil Pig Star forever.

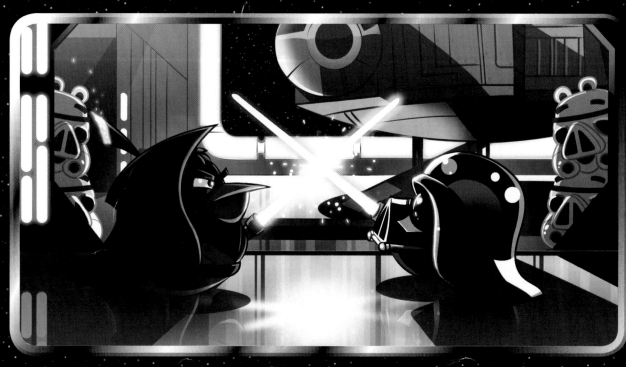

THE EMPIRE OINKS BACK!

But this first great victory was not enough to ensure the continued success of the Bird Rebel Alliance. They found themselves on the run from the Pig Empire and it wasn't long before their frozen base on the ice planet Hoth was invaded by Lard Vader and his troops.

The heroes were forced to split up to evade Vader. Red Skywalker and his faithful droid, R2-EGG2, flew to the planet Dagobah to train with a wise old Jedi called Yoda Bird. Yoda Bird was a harsh taskmaster whose training involved a lot of falling on your head and getting slapped on the beak! As his bruises mounted, Red wondered whether he'd been a little hasty in quitting his old job on the farm!

Meanwhile, Chuck and Terebacca took Princess Stella and C-3PYOLK for a ride across

the galaxy in the *Mighty Falcon* before finding safety in Cloud City, a giant floating nest governed by Chuck's old smuggler pal, Lando Birdissian. But Lando had already made a deal with the Pig Empire to hand over the rebels in exchange for his own freedom – it wasn't a great deal but he was being backed into a corner!

Planets away, Red Skywalker sensed through the Force that his friends were in danger. He cut short his training to go help them.

When Red arrived on Cloud City, Lard Vader was waiting for him. Chuck Solo had been carbon frozen and handed over to the heartless bounty hunter, Boba Fatt – but it was Red who Vader wanted.

"Obi-Wan told me you killed my father," Red squawked angrily as the two clashed.

"No, Red," Vader replied. "I am your father!"

It was all too much for Red, who only escaped by luck, falling into the waiting arms of Terebacca and the *Mighty Falcon* – which was now being piloted by Lando! It seemed Lando was having second thoughts about betraying his old pal Chuck and had decided to side with the Bird Rebels in their darkest hour. But Chuck was lost!

RETURN OF THE JEDI BIRD!

The heroes learned that Boba Fatt had shipped Chuck's frozen body to Jabba the Hog's Palace to repay the debt Chuck owed the crime lord. Stella and Terebacca tried to save Chuck but were captured just after unfreezing him. But they had another ally waiting in the wings. Red arrived, using his newly acquired Force skills to trick Jabba into releasing the whole gang of rebels! Jabba's precious barge was destroyed — and so was he, along with all the treats he'd been selfishly storing!

Just then, news reached the Bird Rebels that the Pig Empire was building a new Pig Star — and this one would be bigger and meaner than the one that they had previously blown up! It was downright obese!

Chuck Solo led a stealth crew, that included Princess Stella and Red Skywalker, to shut down the Pig Star's external force field so that Lando could pilot the *Mighty Falcon* to set off a bomb inside.

As the plan unfolded, Red gave himself up to the Empire, hoping to convince his father — Lard Vader — to see the error of his ways and side with the birds.

Cruel Emperor Piglatine pitted Vader and Skywalker against one another — father against son — egging on the younger bird's anger. But at the last moment, Vader relented and turned on his

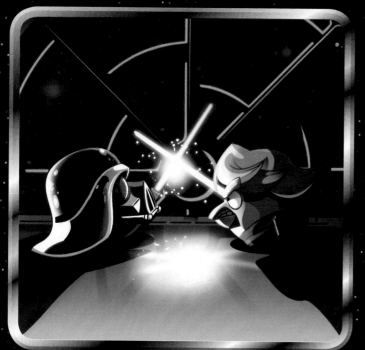

against the new Pig Star and the incomplete battle station started to shake itself apart.

Red hopped on a shuttle to escape the destruction and was soon partying with his old pals, as well as a group of primitive locals called Ewok Birds, on the nearby planet that had housed the force field generator.

It was over – the Bird Rebel Alliance had won, Lard Vader had renounced his greedy ways before dying and the Emperor was dead! Long live the birds!

master, defeating him in a show of furious anger!

At the same moment, Lando finally scored the critical hit

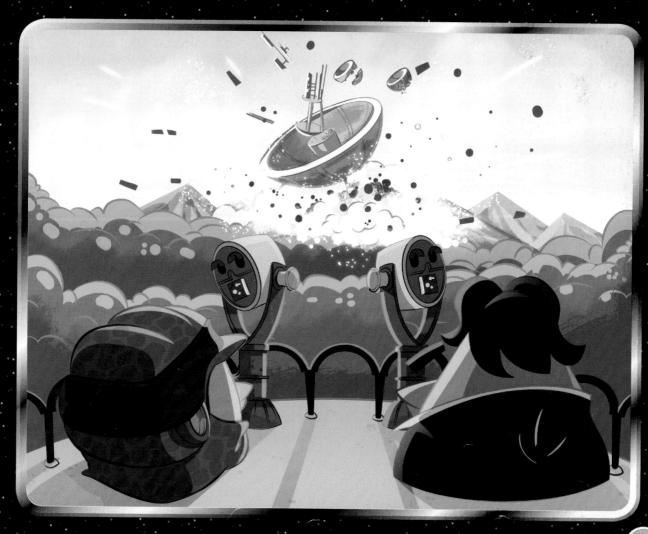

DESIGN A GETAWAY SPACESHIP

SPACESHIP NAME:
LARD VADER'S TIE FIGHTER
CREW: LARD VADER
ARMAMENTS: BLASTERS
TOP SPEED: 80/100

SPACESHIP NAME:
X-WING BIRDFIGHTER
CREW: RED SKYWALKER
ARMAMENTS: BLASTERS
TOP SPEED: 70/100

SPACESHIP NAME:
THE MIGHTY FALCON
CREW: CHUCK "HAM" SOLO
& TEREBACCA
ARMAMENTS: BLASTERS
TOP SPEED: 100/100

SPACESHIP NAME:
TIE FIGHTER
CREW: PIGTROOPER
ARMAMENTS: BLASTERS
TOP SPEED: 60/100

Every hero needs a fast spaceship to get out of trouble. Can you design something that's fast, sleek and armed to the teeth?

SPACESHIP NAME: ...intelal Destroyer

CREW: ...Magnus & jack

ARMAMENTS: ...blasters

TOP SPEED: ...72.../100

RED SKYWALKER

ZAP NOW!

Red Skywalker is a rebel hero who is learning to become a Jedi Bird warrior. Red can be hard-headed and a bit of a know-it-all. He's kind of clumsy, which leads him into incredible scrapes – that's how he got involved in saving Princess Stella Organa from the evil Pig Empire.

As a devotee to the Force, he wants to find The Egg and unravel its secrets... before the pigs get their filthy snouts on it!

X-WING BIRDFIGHTER

LIGHTSABER

STELLA ORGANA

Princess Stella is one of the leaders of the Bird Republic, and would be a prize for any Pigtrooper able to capture and hold her.

She's stubborn, opinionated and expects everyone to obey her, no matter how reckless her commands sometimes seem.

Stella dreams of one day freeing the birds' home planet and destroying the Pig Empire. She fancies Chuck Solo – and she's pretty disappointed in herself about it!

BLOCKADE RUNNER

BIRD REPUBLIC LOGO

CHUCK "HAM" SOLO

Chuck Solo is the captain of the *Mighty Falcon*, the fastest ship in the galaxy. He's a successful junk food smuggler – which is how he got his nickname "Ham" – but these days he runs with the Bird Republic, fighting to free the galaxy from the grip of Emperor Piglatine. Ham acts cocky and confident but most of the time he doesn't know what he's doing!

THE MIGHTY FALCON

BLASTER

TEREBACCA

Terebacca is Chuck's best friend. He's very loyal and sometimes displays a fearsome temper. Terebacca is the co-pilot of the *Mighty Falcon*, and he gets pretty defensive when other people try to tell him how to fly. Terebacca communicates by grunting and staring – and only his buddy Chuck can understand him!

THE MIGHTY FALCON

WEAPON BELT

OBI-WAN KABOOMI

This aging Jedi Bird Warrior is a master of the Force, but he can't always control his explosions! Obi-Wan takes Red under his wing and introduces him to the ways of the Force. He would do everything he could to protect The Egg... if only he knew where it was hidden!

LIGHTSABER

YODA BIRD

LIGHTSABER

Yoda Bird is a very old and wise Jedi Bird Master who helped train Obi-Wan Kaboomi when he was just a young hatchling! Yoda Bird hid The Egg – and he hasn't yet told anyone where he put it! Maybe he's forgotten! Yoda Bird hopes that one day Red Skywalker can master his temper and be trusted with the secret of The Egg.

C-3PYOLK

Merciful circuits! This gold-plated droid is a master of languages and protocol.

C-3PYOLK has been programmed to function only on the Rebel side. He also takes care of plants – though when he speaks to them, no one knows whether they can understand him!

OCCULAR SENSORS

GOLD PLATED

R2-EGG2

Shhh! Don't tell anyone but R2-EGG2 is actually... The Egg in disguise! So that's where Yoda Bird put it! R2's also a handy droid to have around. He contains a lot of knowledge in his circuits and helps Red pilot his X-wing Bird Fighter.

R2-EGG2 and C-3PYOLK are always bickering, but deep down they're best buddies.

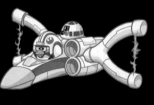

X-WING

THE EGG!

JAWA BIRDS JUNK JOKE PAGE!

What sound does a bird's phone make?
Wing-Wing! Wing-Wing!

What goes cock-a-doodle-don't?
A hen who doesn't want to get up!

What's the difference between the rear of a bird and a lost boat?
One has tail feathers while the other has failed tethers!

What type of bird sounds like a cow?
An E-moo!

Who is the tallest Lard of the Sith?
Giraffe Vader!

What's the difference between a normal calendar and a bird calendar?
Only one shows the days of the beak!

What type of pigs are the most honest?
Pig-TRUE-pers!

Why do hummingbirds hum?
Because they don't know the words!

What do you call a bird who steals things?
Robin!

What do you call a bird that's bigger than a hen?
A moorhen!

Why did the chicken cross the galaxy?
To get to the other side!

ESCAPE FROM THE PIG STAR

Ham and Terebacca are trapped on the Pig Star.
Can you help them find a safe route out?

23

EGG-CHO BASE MAYHEM!

THE BIRD REBELS' ECHO BASE IS BEING OVERRUN BY SNOWPIGS! CAN YOU FIND...

Lard Vader

The *Mighty Falcon*

5 x lightsabers

C-3PYOLK

R2-EGG2

Copypig

Boba Fatt

2 x Pigbots

3 x Imperial droids

4 x Imperial Droids

Pig trooper Commander

10 Blasters

5 Medals

ZAP NOW!

LARD VADER

Lard Vader was once a Jedi Bird warrior called Redkin Skywalker. But he became corrupted by the promises of Emperor Piglatine, and was drawn to the Pork Side. Now, Lard Vader is one of the leaders of the Pig Empire and he is utterly feared throughout the galaxy. Vader wants just one thing – to rule the galaxy. The best way he can think to do this is to find The Egg.

Tie-Fighter

Lightsaber

EMPEROR PIGLATINE

Emperor Piglatine is the absolute ruler of the Pig Empire, through which he controls the galaxy. Piglatine is a very greedy pig – he has banned all the candies and snacks in the whole universe just so that he can keep them all to himself!
However, what he really wants to eat is The Egg!

PIGSTAR

FORCE LIGHTNING

PIGTROOPERS

The Pigtroopers are utterly loyal to Emperor Piglatine and obey his commands.

These well-armed pigs search the galaxy for junk food to bring to their dread master.

Pigtroopers wear different armour for different occasions, including extra warm armour for the snow and sleek armour for riding on their souped up speeder bikes.

Pigtroopers never think for themselves – they're just happy to follow orders, no matter how dumb those orders may be!

TIE-FIGHTER PILOT

AT-AT PILOT

SNOWTROOPER

COPY PIG

HOG GUARDS

The private guards of Emperor Piglatine, these sinister figures are silent witnesses to the Emperor's cruellest decisions. Clad in their unmistakable red armour, these pigs are the most fearsome bodyguards in the universe. Their spiked forks could cut through an egg with ease. So watch out!

SPIKED FORK

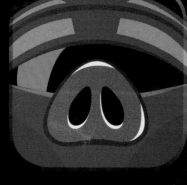

EYE SLIT

ATTACK OF THE COLOUR!

NOW IT'S YOUR TURN TO HONE YOUR COLOURING SKILLS WITH THIS CRITICAL MOMENT FROM THE BATTLE BETWEEN GOOD AND EVIL!

32

TRAPPED!

FOLLOW THE TRACTOR BEAMS TO FIND OUT WHICH PIG DESTROYER HAS SNAGGED PRINCESS STELLA'S SPACESHIP.

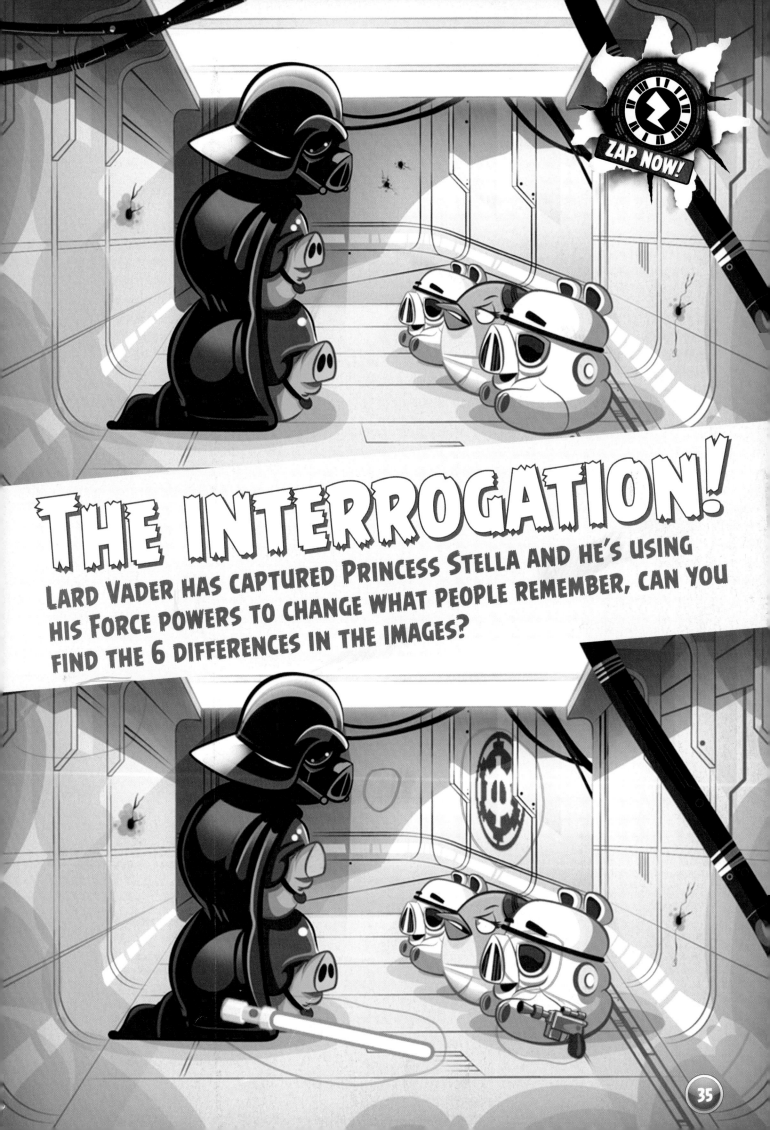

THE INTERROGATION!

LARD VADER HAS CAPTURED PRINCESS STELLA AND HE'S USING HIS FORCE POWERS TO CHANGE WHAT PEOPLE REMEMBER, CAN YOU FIND THE 6 DIFFERENCES IN THE IMAGES?

ZAP NOW!

35

MAY THE COLOURS BE WITH YOU!

ADD SOME COLOUR TO THIS EGG-CITING SCENE!

LIGHTSABER SUDOKU

Curse my metal body! I've been asked to organise these lightsabers but I seem to have got myself in quite a muddle! Can you help complete the grid, ensuring that every line contains only one of each colour, both up-and-down and left-to-right?

ZAP NOW!

REPAIR THE MIGHTY FALCON

CHUCK NEEDS TO MAKE URGENT REPAIRS ON THE MIGHTY FALCON BUT HIS PALS HAVE GONE INTO HIDING WITH THE SPARE PARTS. CAN YOU WORK OUT WHO'S HIDING WHERE AND WITH WHICH DROID?

Clues:
1. R2-EGG2 is on Hoth.
2. Red Skywalker did not go to Cloud City, does not have armour Parts and is not with the Imperial Droid.
3. Princess Stella either went to Tatooine or she has the radar dish.
4. Terebacca does not have the radar dish but he is with C-3PYOLK.
5. The radar dish is with someone who has a Imperial Droid.

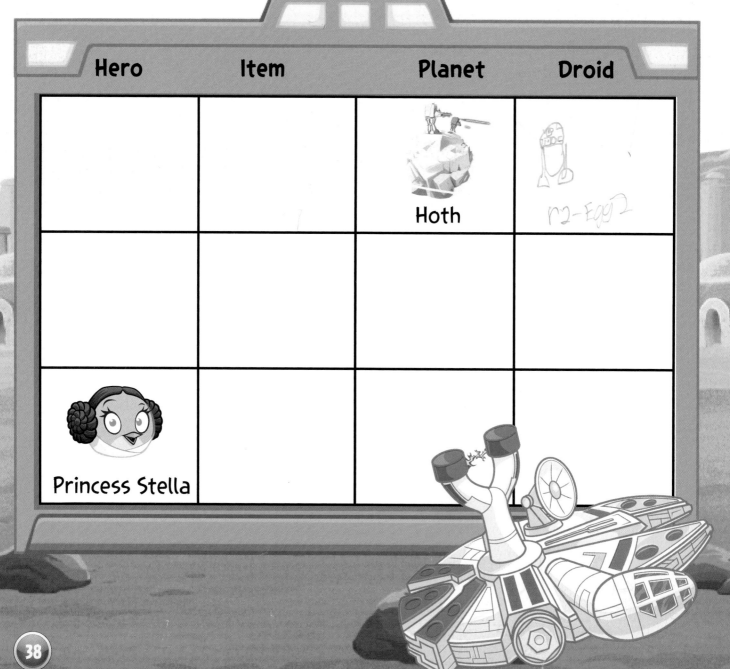

Hero	Item	Planet	Droid
		Hoth	R2-EGG2
Princess Stella			

HUCK'S OLD BUDDY LANDO BIRDISSIAN HAS SENT
IM A MESSAGE IN THE SMUGGLERS SECRET CODE.
AN YOU DECIPHER THE MESSAGE?

KOB FKEFM,
A KUXO KAGGOO U DAJ VWUVK
IH BEPPB VYOOWV UOG LEOM
HIIG AQ WKO UVWOTIAG
HAONG!BIET RUN.
NUQG!!

A=U	N=Q
B=D	O=I
C=F	P=R
D=G	Q=S
E=O	R=T
F=H	S=V
G=J	T=W
H=K	U=E
I=A	V=X
J=L	W=Y
K=M	X=Z
L=N	Y=B
M=P	Z=C

FOLLOWING ORDERS!

THESE CLASSIC MOMENTS FROM RED'S LIFE HAVE BEEN JUMBLED UP. FIGURE OUT THE CORRECT ORDER OF EVENTS AND WRITE YOUR ANSWERS IN THE BOX PROVIDED.

A. Red versus Lard Vader aboard the second Pig Star!

B. Red is trained by Yoda Bird!

C. Red buys the droids from the Jawa Birds!

D. Red meets Chuck and Terebacca in the space cantina!

E. Red and his fellow heroes almost become dinner for the Ewok Birds!

F. Lard Vader reveals that he is Red's father!

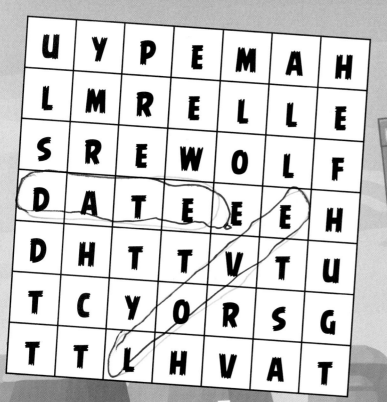

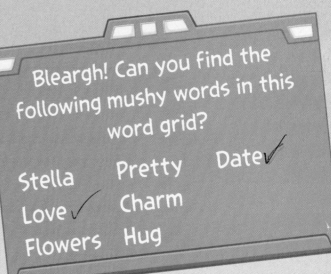

Ham's hidden a secret message in this letter to Stella.

Can you work out what it is?

Q: What did Stella say when she defrosted Ham?

A: Ice to see you!

Stella...

The idea of taking a holiday sounds super. Rebel or Pig, everyone needs to get away from it all every now and then! Nest life can seem pretty boring after a while! Is that selfish of me? On one hand, you might say that it is!

Hoth is far too cold this time of year, however, so perhaps we should go somewhere warmer like Tatooine.

Chuck "Ham" Solo!

Q: What did Stella say when she lost her favourite droid?

A: "Did you See-3PYOLK?"

JABBA'S PARTY PALACE!

JABBA'S HOLDING A PARTY AT HIS PALACE AND EVERYONE'S INVITED. CAN YOU FIND...

Frozen Chuck

4 x hidden blasters

Stella

1 x hidden lightsaber

Terebacca

Grey C3PYOLK

Lando Birdissian

6 x Jawa Birds

Greedork

2 x Ewok Birds

Boba Fatt

6 x burgers

JABBA THE HOG

Ick! Is there any creature more disgusting than Jabba the Hog? Jabba's a crime lord and the king of the smugglers, dealing in black market junk food that the Empire is desperate to get their hands on.
Jabba loves to eat too, and always samples the goods before passing them on. Jabba employs lots of bounty hunters to get his way, including Boba Fatt and Greedork. Jabba used to be Chuck Solo's boss until Chuck let him down and joined the rebellion. Now he wants him back... as a carbon frozen ornament for his stinky palace!

GREEDORK

FROZEN CHUCK SOLO

BOBA FATT

The meanest bounty hunter in the galaxy, Boba Fatt is specially trained to hunt birds – for a fee. Fatt has no loyalty and works for the highest bidder, but he takes special pleasure in tracking down Chuck Solo after Jabba puts a price on the smuggler's beak. Fatt is a master of weapons and cool gadgets. He uses a jet pack to get him out of danger when the feathers start to fly!

SPACESHIP

JETPACK

WANTED POSTER

NOW'S YOUR CHANCE TO PLACE A BOUNTY ON SOMEONE YOU KNOW!

You will need:

1. A scan or photocopy of page 49.
2. Some card (an old cereal or pizza box will do)
3. Paper glue.
4. Scissors (ask an adult to help).
5. A pen or pencil.

Optional:

A photograph of the friend or family member you plan to place your bounty on! Always check with whoever's photo it is first!

Instructions:

1. First you need to decide who you're putting a bounty on. It could be your best friend, your brother or sister, or a parent!

2. Ask an adult to help you cut carefully around the wanted poster following the dotted lines shown. You can glue it to cardboard as well to make it stronger.

3. Fill in the name of the person on whom you're placing your bounty. Add the details of their crimes and how much you're offering in reward money. You can find ideas for possible crimes elsewhere on this page, or come up with your own. Write big — you want this to be seen from a distance!

4. Now you need to add a picture so everyone knows who you're after. You could draw their picture or you could use a photograph and glue it in the space shown. Top Bounty Hunting Tip: Never cut up someone else's photos without permission!

5. Now place the wanted poster somewhere where everyone will see — maybe on your fridge!

Possible Crimes:

Eating the last chocolate biscuit!

Hogging the bathroom!

Talking while you're watching your favourite TV show!

Being smelly!

Making you eat vegetables!

WANTED

THE FOLLOWING IS WANTED BY THE PIG EMPIRE

DEAD OR ALIVE!
FOR THE FOLLOWING CRIMES:
Talking while your watching your favirite TV show

BOUNTY ....∞....... **GALACTIC CREDITS**

ANGER WAS RISING IN THE UNIVERSE...

Young Redkin Skywalker dreamed of becoming a Jedi Bird. So when two famous Jedi Bird warriors called Quail-Gon and Obi-Wan Kaboomi arrived on his doorstep looking for parts to their spaceship, Redkin was only too happy to tag along and learn the ways of the Force. He also fell instantly in love with their royal passenger – Peckmé Amidala.

But all was not going well for the Jedi Birds. When they tried to return Peckmé to her

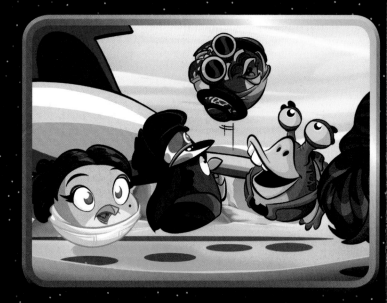

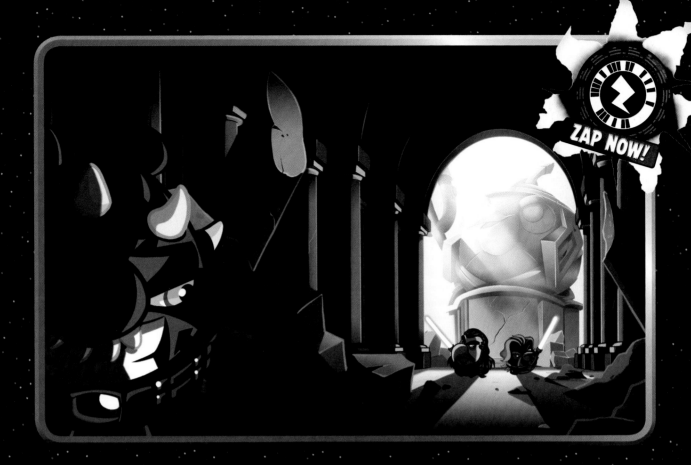

ZAP NOW!

palace on Naboo they were ambushed by the crazy Sith Lard, Darth Moar, who used

a double-bladed lightsaber to fight both Jedi Birds at once! Moar cut down Quail-Gon before Obi-Wan could stop him. But Obi-Wan exploded with so much rage that he made sure Moar wouldn't approach any bird ever again!

Redkin had hoped to train with Quail-Gon. Instead, Obi-Wan took the role of teacher and showed Redkin the ways of the Force. But Redkin was angry and distrustful – he felt certain that the Jedi Bird Council was keeping things from him because they feared his natural ability with the Force.

While the Jedi Bird Council wondered what to do with the impetuous young student, someone else was taking an interest in Redkin. That someone was Senator Piglatine, who was secretly the wicked Sith Lard, Darth Swindle.

Swindle tempted Redkin to learn the ways of the Force with him, promising that it would be faster and more effective than the slow and methodical way of the Jedi Birds. He also had a lot of delicious treats that he promised to share with Redkin if he joined him for training – how could Redkin resist?!

Redkin didn't realise he was being tricked into joining the Pork Side, and when Obi-Wan finally noticed the change it was too late. No longer trusting his old mentor, Redkin fought with Obi-Wan Kaboomi, directing all his anger at him. Obi-Wan was forced to stop the insane Redkin – but it almost cost Redkin his life! Redkin was left terribly wounded at the end of the battle.

Darth Swindle recovered Redkin's scarred body and gave him an artificial suit of armour which would help him breathe and allow him to walk again. With this new suit of armour came a new identity – Redkin was no more, now he was Lard Vader!

As the galaxy went to war, Lard Vader would hunt down the Jedi Birds in the name of his master Emperor Piglatine

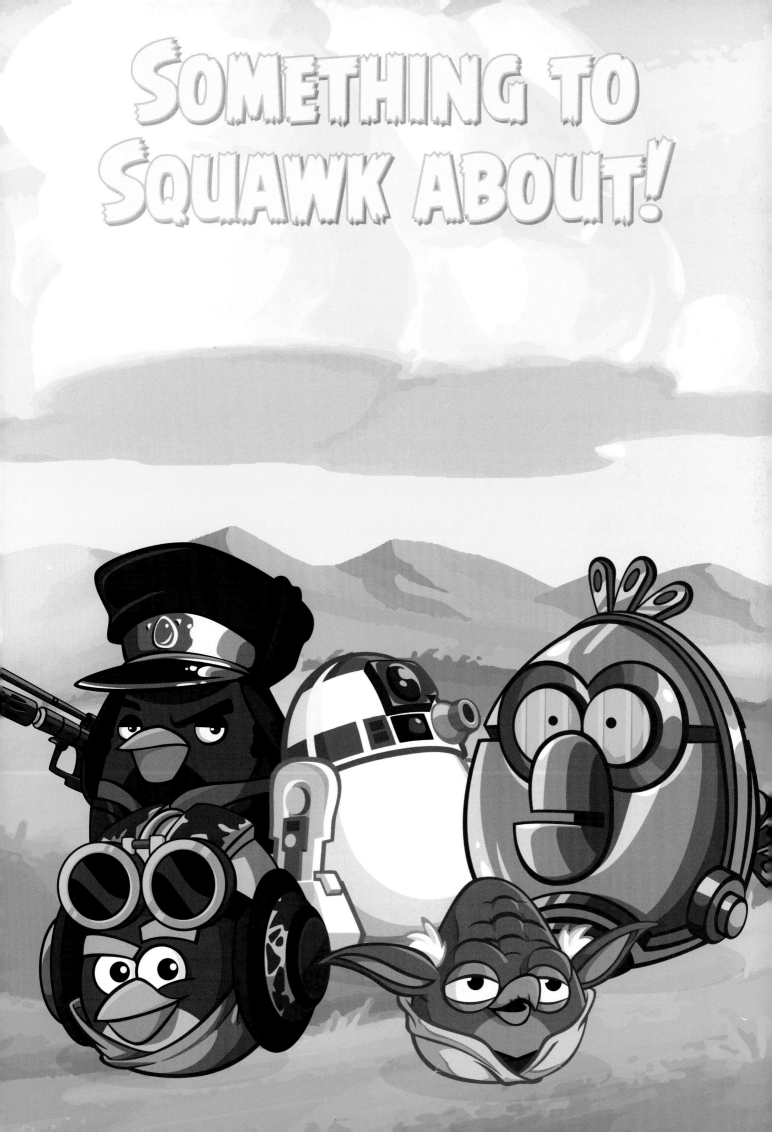

SOMETHING TO SQUAWK ABOUT!

ZAP NOW!

REDKIN SKYWALKER

Redkin Skywalker is a young bird who is very strong in the Force. He is learning to become a Jedi Bird warrior under the supervision of Obi-Wan Kaboomi. But Redkin is impatient and wants to know everything about The Egg. He feels that the members of the Jedi Bird Council are deliberately holding him back so that he may never reach his full potential and challenge them. Angry Redkin finds himself drawn to the Pork Side with its promise of easy power and fast food. Redkin is also drawn to the beauty of Peckmé Amidala – he has had a crush on her ever since he laid eyes on her!

SCAR

LIGHTSABER

QUAIL-GON

Quail-Gon is a powerful Jedi Bird who has a reputation for ignoring the rules to make sure things get done. He's a whiz with a lightsaber and he can tweet information to his fellow Jedi Birds from across the universe. Quail-Gon was the mentor to Obi-Wan Kaboomi, until the day he was killed at the hands of wicked Darth Moar.

LIGHTSABER

YOUNG OBI-WAN KABOOMI

LIGHTSABER

Many years before he goes on his foolish quest with Red Skywalker, Young Obi-Wan Kaboomi was an enthusiastic trainee Jedi Bird under the supervision of Quail-Gon. He's very talented in the Force and is proud of using his abilities. After Quail Gon dies, Obi-Wan agrees to train Redkin. But the impetuous young Redkin proves to be more than a handful!

PECKMÉ AMIDALA

This feisty chick comes from a noble background and grows up to be the queen of her people. She can be so charming that she can shake the ground with a pull of gravity — talk about a magnetic personality! She's very responsible, graceful and sweet! However, once she's annoyed, she has a fiery temper! Peckmé likes Redkin and truly believes there is good deep inside him — even when he starts to go off the rails.

CAPTAIN NAMAKA
PECKMÉ'S BODYGUARD

JAR JAR WINGS

This turkey seems like bit of a goofball and a clown, but his heart's always in the right place. Jar Jar has a very long tongue that is perfectly suited for snagging delicacies and junk food when no one expects it. Yummy! Jar Jar also uses his tongue as a weapon against the evil pigs! Talk about a tongue lashing!

WARRIOR GUNGAN BIRD

YODA BIRD

Many years before he helps Red Skywalker, Yoda Bird is already an old and respected Jedi Bird. He is an elder of the Jedi Bird Council known

LIGHTSABER

for his wisdom and fair-mindedness. He is also known for his often confusing advice! Despite being small, Yoda Bird is a master of the lightsaber. Judge him not by his size!

MOA WINDU

LIGHTSABER

This awesome Jedi Bird is one of the best lightsaber sword fighters of all time. Moa's a high-ranking member of the Jedi Bird Council and he takes his responsibilities very seriously. He strives to be the very best. Moa senses that Redkin Skywalker is not ready to be trained in the Force. He fears that the youngster is too impetuous and too angry to be a Jedi Bird.

DROID SALE

JAWA BIRDS ARE ALWAYS AFTER NEW DROIDS TO SELL AND NOW THEY NEED YOUR HELP! DESIGN A COOL NEW DROID WITH LOTS OF SPECIAL FUNCTIONS. DON'T FORGET TO ADD ITS NAME AND DETAILS ON THE SPECIAL FORM.

I can't abide those Jawa Birds, R2!

DROID FOR SALE:

DROID NAME: ......Star4d!......

INTELLIGENCE: ...80../100

SPECIAL ABILITIES: ......blaststuff....
......and bdork things easy...

THE PODRACE CHASE!

FANCY YOUR CHANCES ON THE PODRACE CIRCUIT? THEN TRY THIS GAME FOR 2-4 PLAYERS.

You will need:

2-4 players.

Counters (you may cut out the counters from this page, or make your own).

A dice.

How to Play:

1. Each player chooses a podracer and places it on the starting grid.
2. Roll to see who starts – highest goes first (roll again if two people get the same!).
3. Each player makes their way around the track, following the instructions on each square.
4. The winner is the one who reaches the finish line first! Simple!

Optional Extra Rule:

Podraces usually run three laps. So why not go around three times before the winner is declared. If you do this, you will need to have a pencil and paper to keep track of who has completed each lap!

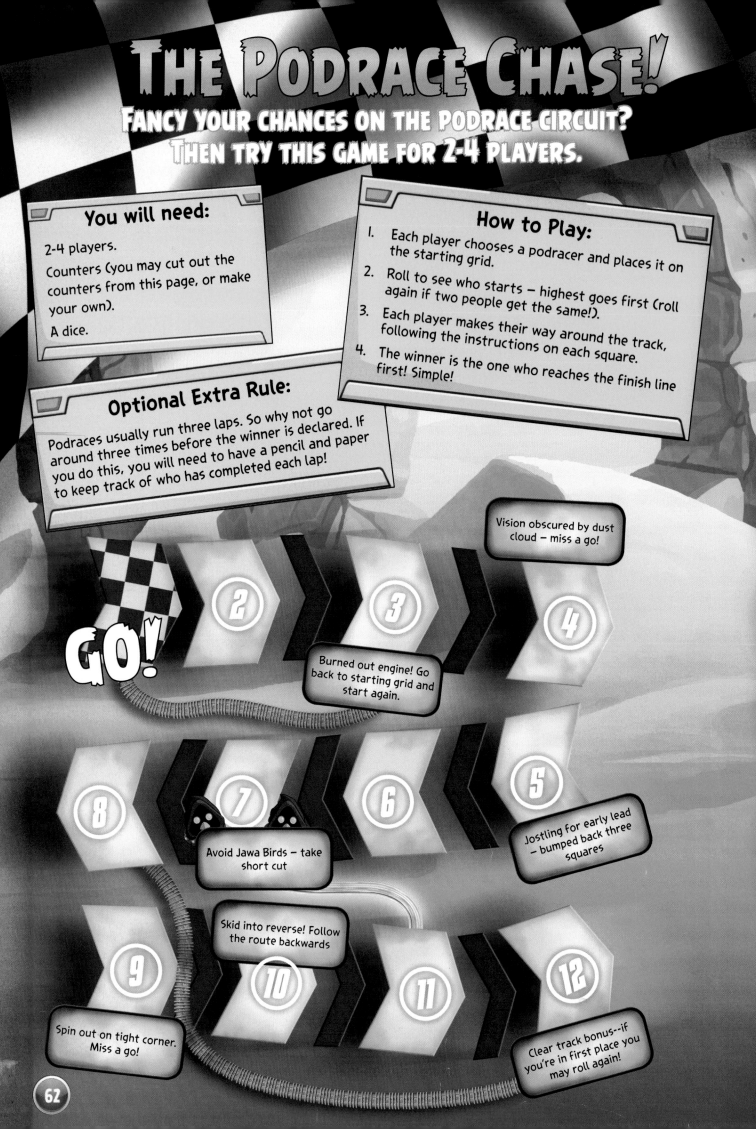

GO!

2

3
Burned out engine! Go back to starting grid and start again.

4
Vision obscured by dust cloud – miss a go!

5
Jostling for early lead – bumped back three squares

6

7
Avoid Jawa Birds – take short cut

8

Skid into reverse! Follow the route backwards

9
Spin out on tight corner. Miss a go!

10

11

12
Clear track bonus--if you're in first place you may roll again!

Cut out these counters or make your own!

13

14 — Tipped off by Yoda Bird – dart ahead along the arrow

15

Force boost – if you're in any position other than first you may roll again!

Sudden sand storm forces you to slow down. On your next turn: if you roll 1, 2 or 3 move ahead 1, if you roll 4, 5 or 6, move 2!

16 — Avoid Tusken Raider Pigs – speed ahead two squares!

17

18

Last place bonus – if you're in last place, roll again!

Energy cells running low – on your next turn, roll the dice twice and take the lowest number for your go!

19

20

21

22 — R2-EGG2 directs you to a shortcut.

23

24 — Taken the wrong route. Whatever you roll on your next go – go backwards!

25

26 — Spin out! Miss your next turn unless you throw a 1!

27

Last minute foul play damages engine – go back via the pits

28

29

30

LIGHTSABER DUEL!

ADD SOME COLOUR TO THIS SPECTACULAR CLASH.

NAVIGATE THE GALAXY

ZAP NOW!

You're on a mercy mission and need to navigate around the galaxy. There's just one catch, you have to reach the planets in the right order. So, power up your engines and get to work!

FLIGHT ORDER:
Tatooine - Hoth - Dagobah - Cloud City

HOTH

TATOOINE

CLOUD CITY

PIG STAR

DAGOBAH

A B C

65

REBELS TO THE CORE!

DARTH SWINDLE

Also known as Piglatine, a representative in the Galactic Council, Darth Swindle is one of the foulest and most corrupt creatures in the universe and is the supreme power of the Pork Side. This wicked piggy fools the Jedi Birds entirely — but in reality, he's a Lard of the Sith just waiting to make his move.

Swindle's appetite for junk food has no limits, and his selfishness is without equal. Though unarmed, Swindle's special power is the ability to blast deadly force lightning from his hands. Never turn your back on him!

Darth Swindle's greatest triumph is corrupting the impressionable young Redkin Skywalker, turning him into his deadly assistant — Lard Vader. One day soon, Darth Swindle will become the Emperor of the Universe.

FORCE LIGHNING

LARD VADER

Lard Vader wasn't always loyal to the Pork Side. He started out as apprentice Jedi Bird Redkin Skywalker but over time he was drawn to the Pork Side, believing it to be a quicker and easier path to the power and junk food he desired. Now, Lard Vader is an utterly evil creature who hunts the outlawed Jedi Birds. He is a superb lightsaber fighter and has many wicked Pork Side powers, including moving objects with his mind and strangling his foes without even touching them! But Lard Vader craves even more power and he secretly desires The Egg so that he can overthrow his master, Darth Swindle, and take control of the universe himself!

REDKIN · SITH

LIGHTSABER

COUNT DODO

An especially sinister Lard of the Sith, Count Dodo was once a Jedi Bird warrior just like Lard Vader. Dodo was trained by Yoda himself in the ways of the Force – but he turned to the Pork Side because he believes that pigs are superior to birds and other creatures. Dodo is a master with the lightsaber, making the most complex moves look effortless.

LIGHTSABER

DARTH MOAR

Darth Moar is another Lard of the Sith. This crazy, red-faced pig is so angry he can never calm down! Moar was introduced to the Pork Side from a very young age when Darth Swindle tempted him with junk food. Moar has never looked back. He's armed with a double-bladed lightsaber which is twice as deadly as the weapons of the Jedi Birds! He killed brave Quail Gon. But he ultimately met his match in Obi-Wan Kaboomi, who killed him.

LIGHTSABER

GENERAL GRUNTER

General Grunter is part droid, part pig! He is the commander of the battle pig army. His pork circuitry makes him lightning-fast and ensures that he never tires. He takes special delight in battling with Jedi Birds and is a master of their signature weapon, the lightsaber.

LIGHTSABER

BATTLE PIGS

Battle Pigs are droids who fight on the Pork Side under the commands of General Grunter. Heavily armed and appearing in almost infinite numbers, these wicked droids invade peace-loving planets to steal more junk food and treats for the Pork Federation. They were designed to have the best qualities of the pigs – but something went wrong with the programming so that they are actually rather stupid and clumsy!

BLASTER

CAN YOU HELP WITH THIS STORY? WE'VE GIVEN YOU THE START AND THE END – BUT YOU'LL NEED TO MAKE UP THE REST AND DRAW IT IN THE PANELS.

They weren't counting on the old Ham Solo charm!

UNLEASH THE PIGS!

CAN YOU FIND THE 6 DIFFERENCES IN THE IMAGES?

LAW OF THE JUMBLE!

CAN YOU UNPICK THESE CHARACTER NAMES AND FIND OUT WHICH OF THE CHARACTERS ISN'T THERE?

RGEEDNKEIRNASLKGYRWUANLTKEERR

DJAARRTJHASRWWIINNDGLSE

POEBCIKWMAENAKMAIBDOAOLMAI

CDOAURNTTHDMOODAOR

JAR JAR'S JOKES!

What do you call a Jedi Bird who goes up and down on a string?

Yo-Yoda!

Who is the biggest Jedi Bird?

Q-Whale-Gon!

How does Peckmé pay for her clothes?

In Ami-dollars.

Where does Redkin Skywalker sleep?

In his bedkin!

How do Jedi Birds eat their dinner?

With knives, Force and spoons!

Why did Yoda Bird eat his dinner with a knife and spoon?

Because he had to avoid the Fork Side!

What do the Jedi Birds do when their council chamber is too warm?

They open a Windu!

What do you call a cow who turns to the Pork Side?

Calf Swindle!

Who is the most musical hero bird?

Jar Jar Sings!

What do you call a Pork Sider who's good at number puzzles?

Count Su-Dooku!

Where do bounty hunters paint pictures?

On a Zam Easel!

Who is the most flashy hero bird?

Jar Jar Blings!

What do you call a droid who paints pictures?

Arty-EGG2.

ANSWERS...

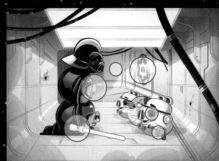
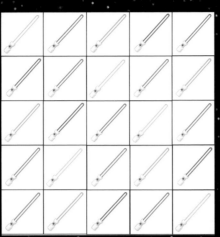

Visit www.pedigreebooks.com

Visit pedigreebooks.com to discover more on the 2015 Angry Birds™ Star Wars™ Annual, plus other titles in our range. Scan with your mobile device to learn more.

Pedigree Books, Beech Hill House, Walnut Gardens, Exeter EX4 4DH